Nobody's Perfect, Charlie Brown

Selected Cartoons from YOU CAN DO IT, CHARLIE BROWN Vol. 1

Charles M. Schulz

CORONET BOOKS
Hodder Fawcett, London

Coronet edition 1969
Second impression 1970
Third impression 1972
Fourth impression 1973
Fifth impression 1974
Sixth impression 1975

Printed and bound in Great Britain for
Coronet Books,
Hodder Fawcett,
St. Paul's House, Warwick Lane,
London, EC4P 4AH
by Hazell Watson & Viney Ltd,
Aylesbury, Bucks

ISBN 0 340 10541 0

DID YOU EVER STOP TO THINK THAT EVERY DAY IS SOMEBODY'S BIRTHDAY?

NO MATTER WHAT DAY IT IS, SOMEBODY IN THE WORLD HAS THAT DAY FOR A BIRTHDAY!

HAVE YOU EVER THOUGHT ABOUT THAT, CHARLIE BROWN?

NO, I CAN'T REALLY SAY THAT I HAVE...

YOU'RE GOING TO HAVE TROUBLE WHEN YOU GET TO COLLEGE!

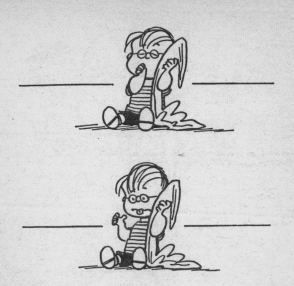

I WONDER IF THE STARS REALLY DO HAVE LITTLE POINTS...

NO, THIS IS DUE TO OUR ASTIGMATISM, WHICH IS A DISTORTION OF VISION CAUSED BY IRREGULARITIES IN THE SURFACE OF THE CORNEA

MY OPHTHALMOLOGIST SAYS THAT A SLIGHT DEGREE OF ASTIGMATISM IS NORMAL, AND THIS KEEPS US FROM SEEING THE STARS AS ROUND DOTS OF LIGHT

TELL YOUR OPHTHALMOLOGIST HE'S RUINED MY STAR-GAZING!

WHY COULDN'T McCOVEY HAVE HIT THE BALL JUST THREE FEET HIGHER?

I NEED YOUR HELP, SNOOPY...

I WANT YOU TO START SCANNING THE SKIES...IF YOU SEE A LIGHT BLUE KITE, THAT'S MY BLANKET...

KEEP LOOKING UP...THAT'S THE WAY...LET ME KNOW THE MINUTE YOU SEE ANYTHING...

THIS IS RISKY...SOMEONE IS BOUND TO COME ALONG AND TICKLE ME UNDER THE CHIN!

LOOK AT THE LETTERS I'VE BEEN GETTING, CHARLIE BROWN..

HERE'S ONE FROM SOMEONE WHO SAW MY BLANKET FLYING OVER CANDLESTICK PARK IN SAN FRANCISCO, AND HERE'S ONE FROM OHIO, AND HERE'S ONE FROM MINNEAPOLIS...

HERE'S A PERSON WHO THOUGHT SHE SAW MY BLANKET FLYING OVER THE GRAND CANYON...

IT SOUNDS LIKE YOUR BLANKET IS REALLY GETTING AROUND

IT ALWAYS DID WANT TO TRAVEL..

I'M QUITTING!

IT'S RIDICULOUS TO KEEP PLAYING ON A TEAM THAT ALWAYS LOSES!

THIS TEAM WILL NEVER AMOUNT TO ANYTHING! IT'S JUST GOING TO LOSE, LOSE, LOSE, LOSE !!!

I REFUSE TO PLAY LEFT-FIELD FOR A SINKING SHIP!

IN A WAY THIS IS KIND OF INTERESTING...

THIS IS MY CHANCE TO OBSERVE AT FIRST HAND WHAT HAPPENS TO A BASEBALL MANAGER WHEN HIS TEAM DESERTS HIM...

HERE IS A MAN DEDICATED TO HIS JOB...SUDDENLY HE IS WITHOUT A TEAM..WHAT DOES HE DO? WHERE DOES HE GO?

HE GOES HOME!
☆ SIGH ☆

STOP GRINNING AT ME!

YOU SAY MY BEING A SLOW READER IS NOT CAUSED BY NEEDING GLASSES?

PROBABLY NOT...

SLOW READING IN CHILDREN IS OFTEN THE RESULT OF "MIXED BRAIN DOMINANCE"...A PERSON IS RIGHT-HANDED BECAUSE THE LEFT SIDE OF HIS BRAIN IS DOMINANT...

NOW, IF YOU ARE AMBIDEXTROUS, OR IF YOU HAVE BEEN FORCED TO WRITE WITH THE WRONG HAND, THIS MAY PRODUCE "MIXED BRAIN DOMINANCE"...

IF THIS IS TRUE, WE CAN RULE OUT POOR VISION AS THE CAUSE OF YOUR SLOW READING..

HAVE YOU RULED OUT STUPIDITY?

DO YOU PARTICIPATE MUCH IN KINDERGARTEN, SALLY?

I TRY NOT TO...I'M SORT OF HOLDING BACK...

FOR INSTANCE, YESTERDAY THE TEACHER WANTED ALL OF US TO GO TO THE CHALK BOARD AND DRAW, BUT I GOT OUT OF IT...

I TOLD HER IT WAS HARD FOR ME BECAUSE OF MY BURSITIS!

JUST A MINUTE! HOLD EVERYTHING!

SAY, "OH, DEAR SISTER, WITH THE SWEET FACE AND BEAUTIFUL SMILE, MAY I HAVE A PIECE OF DIVINITY?"

OH, DEAR SISTER, WITH THE SWEET FACE AND BEAUTIFUL SMILE, MAY I HAVE A PIECE OF DIVINITY?

FOR DIVINITY I'LL SAY ANYTHING, NO MATTER HOW NAUSEATING!!

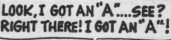

DEAR GREAT PUMPKIN,
I AM LOOKING FORWARD TO YOUR ARRIVAL ON HALLOWEEN NIGHT.

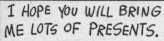

I HOPE YOU WILL BRING ME LOTS OF PRESENTS.

EVERYONE TELLS ME YOU ARE A FAKE, BUT I BELIEVE IN YOU.

SINCERELY,
LINUS VAN PELT

P.S. IF YOU REALLY ARE A FAKE, DON'T TELL ME. I DON'T WANT TO KNOW.

STRIKE THREE!

THIS BAT IS NO GOOD! IT'S TOO LIGHT! THAT BALL THEY'RE USING IS NO GOOD EITHER!

HOW CAN ANYBODY HIT WHEN THE SUN IS SO BRIGHT? I BAT BETTER WHEN IT'S CLOUDY! IT'S TOO DUSTY OUT THERE, TOO!

I CAN'T HIT WELL WHEN THE WIND IS BLOWING! THAT BAT I WAS USING IS TOO SHORT! IT'S HARD TO SEE THE BALL TODAY! YOU CAN'T HIT A BALL WHEN THE BAT IS TOO THIN! I THINK THEIR PITCHER IS..

GOOD GRIEF!

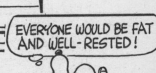

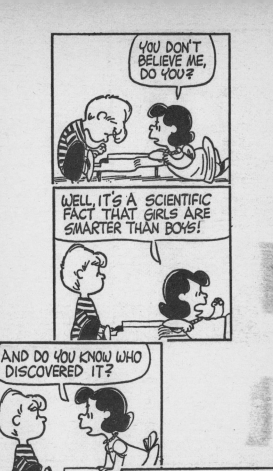

And don't forget about all the other PEANUTS books in CORONET Book editions. Good Grief! More than THREE MILLION of them in paperback! See the check-list overleaf.

© 1970 United Feature Syndicate, Inc.

Wherever Paperbacks Are Sold

Peanuts

- ☐ 02709 6   You're a Winner, Charlie Brown (1)   30p
- ☐ 02710 X   For the Love of Peanuts (2)   30p
- ☐ 04491 8   Good Ol' Snoopy (3)   30p
- ☐ 04409 8   Who do you think you are, Charlie Brown? (4)   30p
- ☐ 04305 9   Fun with Peanuts (5)   30p
- ☐ 04295 8   Here Comes Snoopy (6)   25p
- ☐ 04318 0   You're My Hero, Charlie Brown (7)   25p
- ☐ 04406 3   This Is Your Life, Charlie Brown (8)   25p
- ☐ 04294 X   Let's Face It, Charlie Brown (9)   25p
- ☐ 04407 1   Slide! Charlie Brown, Slide! (10)   25p
- ☐ 04405 5   All This And Snoopy, Too (11)   25p
- ☐ 10788 X   Good Grief, Charlie Brown! (12)   30p
- ☐ 10595 X   Here's To You, Charlie Brown (13)   25p
- ☐ 10673 5   Very Funny, Charlie Brown (15)   30p
- ☐ 10760 X   We're On Your Side, Charlie Brown! (16)   25p
- ☐ 10761 8   Hey, Peanuts (17)   25p
- ☐ 12838 0   You're a Brave Man, Charlie Brown (18)   30p
- ☐ 12786 4   We Love You, Snoopy (19)   25p
- ☐ 12609 4   Peanuts for Everybody (20)   30p
- ☐ 12614 0   You're Too Much, Charlie Brown (21)   30p
- ☐ 12618 3   Here Comes Charlie Brown (22)   30p
- ☐ 12521 7   You've Done It Again, Charlie Brown (23)   25p
- ☐ 12543 8   The Wonderful World of Peanuts (24)   30p
- ☐ 12520 9   Charlie Brown and Snoopy (25)   25p
- ☐ 12544 6   What Next, Charlie Brown? (26)   30p
- ☐ 15135 8   You're The Greatest, Charlie Brown (27)   30p
- ☐ 15829 8   It's For You, Snoopy (28)   25p
- ☐ 15828 X   Have It Your Way, Charlie Brown (29)   25p
- ☐ 15698 8   You're Not For Real, Snoopy (30)   30p
- ☐ 15696 1   You're a Pal, Snoopy (31)   25p
- ☐ 16712 2   What Now, Charlie Brown? (32)   25p
- ☐ 17322 X   You're Something Special, Snoopy (33)   25p
- ☐ 17417 X   You've Got A Friend, Charlie Brown (34)   25p
- ☐ 17844 2   Take It Easy, Charlie Brown (35)   30p
- ☐ 17861 2   Who Was That Dog I Saw You With, Charlie Brown? (36)   30p
- ☐ 18303 9   There's No-one Like You, Snoopy (37)   25p
- ☐ 18663 1   Your Choice, Snoopy (38)   25p
- ☐ 18831 6   Try It Again, Charlie Brown (39)   30p
- ☐ 19550 9   You've Got it Made, Snoopy (40)   25p

All these books are available at your local bookshop or newsagent, or can be ordered direct from the publisher. Just tick the titles you want and fill in the form below.

....

CORONET BOOKS, P.O. Box 11, Falmouth, Cornwall.

Please send cheque or postal order, and allow the following for postage and packing:

U.K. and Eire – 15p for the first book plus 5p per copy for each additional book ordered to a maximum charge of 50p.

Overseas Customers and B.F.P.O. – please allow 20p for the first book and 10p per copy for each additional book.

Name..

Address..

....

....